A Teddy Horsley

Autun

CW00865002

Betsy Bear learns about death
Based on John 12.24-25

by Leslie J Francis and Nicola M Slee
Pictures by Laura Cooper

The Bear facts:
The Teddy Horsley Bible Series is designed to build bridges between the young child's day to day experiences of the world and major biblical themes and stories.

Both authors work in church-related institutions of education. Nicola Slee is Director of Studies at the Aston Training Scheme in Birmingham. Leslie Francis is Professor of Pastoral Theology at the University of Wales, Lampeter, and Trinity College, Carmarthen. The illustrator, Laura Cooper, is a teacher and artist.

The Teddy Horsley Series is a result of extensive research into the religious development of young children, and the authors' and illustrator's wide experience of educational work in schools and churches.

Published by:
National Christian Education Council
1020 Bristol Road
Selly Oak
Birmingham
B29 6LB

British Library Cataloguing in Publication Data:
A catalogue record for this book is available from the British Library.

Text © Leslie J Francis and Nicola M Slee 1996
Illustrations © National Christian Education Council 1996

Unless otherwise stated, quotations from the Bible are from the Good News Bible, published by the Bible Societies/Collins, © American Bible Society, New York, 1966, 1971, 1976.

ISBN 0-7197-0885-0
First published 1996
Printed in England

The summer holidays are over and Betsy Bear is feeling sad.

She bends down to touch the earth.
Already the insects are sleepy.

She misses the bright colours of the butterflies.

Betsy Bear looks up in the sky.
Already the birds are flying away.

She misses the happy song of the swallows.

Betsy Bear looks down at the ground.
Already the flowers are fading.

She misses the rich scent of the roses.

Betsy Bear stretches out to touch the fruit trees.
Already the branches are bare.

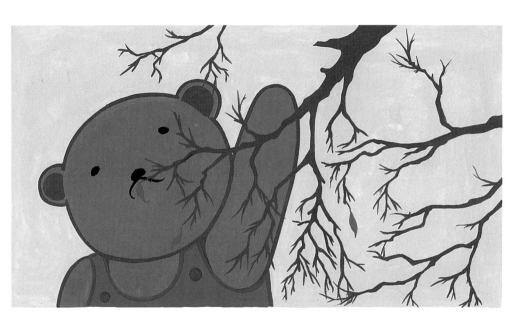

She misses the fresh taste of the plums.

After tea Betsy Bear goes outside to play.
Already the world grows cold and dark.

She misses the warm feeling of the light evening.

Betsy Bear is feeling sad.
She misses the life of summer.

The long winter days are over and Betsy Bear
feels the stirring of new life.

She bends down to talk with the insects.

She sees the new life in their wings.

Betsy Bear looks up to see the birds in the sky.

She hears the new life in their song.

Betsy Bear looks down at the roses in the park.

She smells the new life in the flowers.

Betsy Bear stretches out to touch the strawberry
plants.

She tastes the new life in the fruit.

Betsy Bear knows that death is followed by new life.

In *Autumn*, Betsy Bear's experience of death and life in the cycle of the seasons brings alive for her the Christian conviction of resurrection, and the necessity of the death of the old so that the new can be born.

I am telling you the truth: a grain of wheat remains no more than a single grain unless it is dropped into the ground and dies. If it does die, then it produces many grains. Whoever loves his own life will lose it; whoever hates his own life in this world will keep it for life eternal.

John 12.24-25

The following questions suggest further ways of developing the links between the Bible passage and the young child's experience.

Talk about summer and autumn:
    What do you enjoy doing in summer?
    What do you enjoy seeing in summer?
    What makes you happy in summer?
    What do you miss doing in autumn?
    What do you miss seeing in autumn?
    What makes you sad in autumn?
    What do you look forward to seeing next summer?

Talk about the story:
    Why was Betsy Bear sad?
    What taste did she miss?
    What colours did she miss?
    What sound did she miss?
    What smell did she miss?
    What feeling did she miss?
    What new life did she enjoy after the winter was over?

Think some more about the story:

    What else might Betsy Bear have missed at the end of the summer?

    What other tastes, colours, sounds, smells and feelings?

    What else might she have looked forward to seeing again next summer?

    What other tastes, colours, sounds, smells and feelings?

Think about the Bible passage:

    Have you ever planted a seed in the garden? Or an apple or orange pip in a plant pot? Or an avocado stone in a jam jar?

    What did you do with the seed (or pip or stone)?

    What happened to the seed (or pip or stone)?

    Did it seem a long time while you waited for the first signs of new life?

    What were the first signs of new life?

Titles in the series

Other publications to help young children explore the Bible

Bible Storytime

Six books each containing twenty Bible stories from the Old and New Testaments, retold for the under sevens with related activities and prayer ideas.

Friezes

With clear, bold outlines for easy colouring and cutting out, NCEC friezes are ideal for use with children of all ages. As well as making traditional friezes, most of the material can be used to make 3-dimensional scenes. Based on a variety of themes: